Highlights™
WHICH WAY USA™

FLORIDA

Written by
Curtis Slepian

Illustrated by
C. B. Canga

Welcome to Florida!

Get ready to go to the Sunshine State. Join Tripp and Scout as they try to hit a big-league fastball, train in zero-g like astronauts, and hitch a ride on an Everglades airboat. Collect fun facts and solve puzzles as they race from one end of Florida to the other!

YOUR WHICH WAY USA TEAMMATES

Tripp Wilson
Tripp wants to search for the legendary Fountain of Youth.

Scout Sanchez
Scout wants to stare into the eyes of an Everglades alligator.

You Can Help Tripp and Scout!

At every stop on the race, Tripp and Scout must complete a challenge. You have a job to do, too. The pages of the race are filled with all kinds of puzzles. Solve them to collect bonus points. Tripp and Scout will need your points to win the race.

Go!

YOUR WHICH WAY USA OPPONENTS

Kareem Cheese and Shelly
For these sandwich-store owners, winning races like this is their bread and butter.

Zig and Zag
When these twin skateboarders get on a roll they are "wheelie" tough to beat.

Mel Box and Fred Ex
Neither rain, snow, sleet, nor hail will keep these former mail carriers from delivering a win.

TABLE OF CONTENTS

And They're Off!

The four Which Way teams arrive in Orlando—along with plenty of other people. Florida gets about 85 million visitors each year, and 50 million of them come to Orlando! The teams meet downtown at the huge Orange County Convention Center. Then the race begins! Orlando is packed with fun places to visit, and each team is heading to a different destination.

Tripp uses his tablet to figure out how to go. Scout grabs his arm and says, "Let's take this bus. It's leaving right now!"

You can help Tripp and Scout! Follow each path from start to finish to see where each set of racers is heading. If you do, you'll earn 10 points on page 29.

Orlando Wetlands Park

Orlando Science Center

Farmers' Market

Walt Disney World

Answer on page 30

5

Fowl Play

Tripp and Scout arrive at the world's most popular theme park, Walt Disney World. More than 17 million people come here each year. A girl hands the team Mickey Mouse ears to put on. She tells them that they have to locate another famous cartoon character: Donald Duck.

"Donald quacks me up," Tripp says.

"The joke's on us if we don't find that duck soon," Scout says.

You can help Tripp and Scout while they search for Donald! The names of 15 types of ducks are hidden in this word search. Circle them all, then look below the grid.

Word List

BUFFLEHEAD
CANVASBACK
CRESTED
HARLEQUIN
KING EIDER
MALLARD
MANDARIN
MASKED
MOTTLED
MUSCOVY
PINK-EARED
RUDDY
SMEW
TORRENT
WOOD

```
H A R L E Q U I N J U
T S M T D R P M M C D
R N U O U O A T A R R
E I E D T N O N S E A
D S D R D T V W K S L
I Y M A R A L T E T L
E O R E S O N E D E A
G I M B W Y T B D D M
N D A E H E L F F U B
I C P I N K E A R E D
K M U S C O V Y I L L
```

Did you circle all the words? Now write the leftover letters here, in order from left to right and top to bottom. They spell out the answer to this riddle—and will earn you 10 points on page 29.

What did the duck say when buying a tube of lip balm?

__ __.

Spring Fever

Tripp and Scout rush up the east coast and arrive at St. Augustine. Founded in 1565, it is the oldest city in the United States. The Which Way Kids race to the Fountain of Youth Archaeological Park. According to the legend, drinking water from the Fountain of Youth makes a person young again.

Scout's task is to pour a cup of this spring water into an empty cup—while blindfolded! Tripp calls out directions. "Did you say go left?" Scout asks.

"Right, left!" Tripp says.

You can help Tripp and Scout! Use the map to answer these questions about Florida. Map puzzles earn a double bonus, so this will score you 20 points on page 29.

1. **What is the state capital?**
   a. Miami
   b. Tallahassee
   c. Orlando

2. **In 1961, who was the first American launched into space?**
   a. John Glenn
   b. Alan Shepard
   c. Neil Armstrong

3. **Which city in Florida gets the most rain?**
   a. Pensacola
   b. Fort Lauderdale
   c. Key West

4. **Osceola was the leader of what tribe?**
   a. Apalachee
   b. Uzita
   c. Seminole

5. **From which country did the U.S. get Florida in 1819?**
   a. England
   b. Spain
   c. Albania

6. **In which direction does the St. Johns River flow?**
   a. East to west
   b. North to south
   c. South to north

7. **How many golf courses are in Florida?**
   a. Fewer than 250
   b. 1,000
   c. More than 1,250

8. **What is Florida's state seashell?**
   a. Zebra mussel
   b. Horse conch
   c. Cow conch

9. **Which Florida city has the largest population?**
   a. Jacksonville
   b. Sarasota
   c. Miami

10. **What is Florida's state song?**
    a. "When You Wish Upon a Star"
    b. "Swanee River"
    c. "The Heat Is On"

Answer on page 30

Spitting Images

Everyone sprints northwest to Monticello. Each year, this small town holds a Watermelon Festival. The four crews arrive before the festival takes place, but they compete in their own version of a festival event: a watermelon-seed-spitting contest. The teams line up to see who can spit seeds the farthest. The world's best can spit seeds more than 60 feet!

Tripp whispers to Scout, "My computer says to bounce the seeds along the ground to get distance." Scout can't answer— her mouth is full!

You can help Tripp and Scout! Find 10 pairs of matching watermelon slices. If you do, you'll earn 10 bonus points on page 29.

10

Answer on page 30

Hide and Seek

The next leg of the race is in the Apalachicola National Forest, the largest national forest in Florida. Tripp and Scout must find a cypress grove and take a photo of a wood stork.

Scout points to trees in a swamp and says, "I think those are cypress."

"Yes, they're *tree-rific*!" Tripp says with a whoop.

"There's the bird," Scout says. "Better take a photo fast!"

You can help Tripp and Scout! While they take a snapshot, focus on finding the objects in this Hidden Pictures® puzzle. If you do, you'll earn 10 points on page 29.

glove

wishbone

lollipop

star

ball of yarn

teacup

cap

baseball bat

fork

necktie

artist's brush

comb

kite

saw

Answer on page 30

13

Screwball Baseball

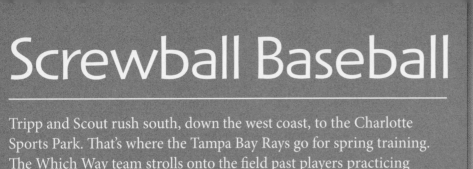

Tripp and Scout rush south, down the west coast, to the Charlotte Sports Park. That's where the Tampa Bay Rays go for spring training. The Which Way team strolls onto the field past players practicing baseball drills.

The duo's task is to hit a ball thrown by a pitcher. The hurler sizzles a fastball past Tripp. "Keep your eye on the ball," shouts Scout.

"How?" he says. "I can't even see it."

You can help Tripp and Scout! While they take their swings, solve this What's Wrong?® puzzle. If you circle at least 20 silly things, you'll earn 10 points on page 29.

BALL		STRIK
3		10
	1 2 3	
RAYS	0 0 1	
?	0 0 2	

Answer on page 30

Clowning Around

The next stop is the "Circus Capital of the World." Sarasota was once the home of the famous Ringling Brothers and Barnum & Bailey Circus. Today several circuses set up tents here. Tripp and Scout head to one of them.

They must perform as clowns under the big top. Tripp tries to make the audience laugh by falling down. As Scout wobbles on a unicycle, Tripp calls, "That thing needs training wheels!"

16

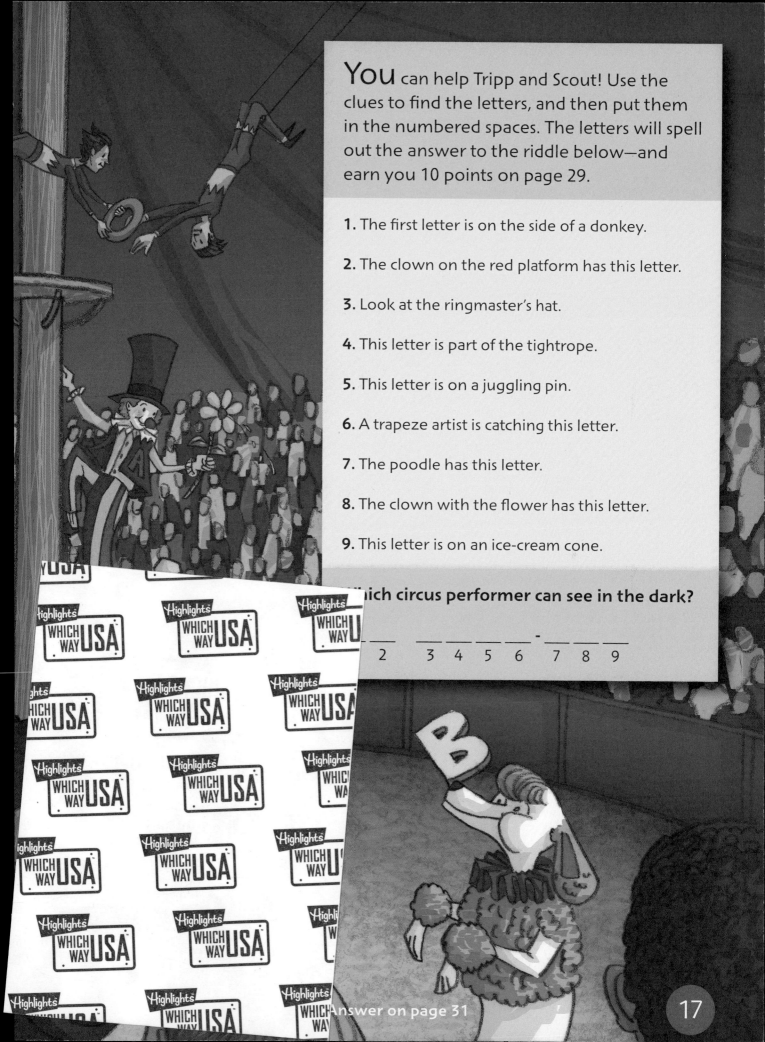

You can help Tripp and Scout! Use the clues to find the letters, and then put them in the numbered spaces. The letters will spell out the answer to the riddle below—and earn you 10 points on page 29.

1. The first letter is on the side of a donkey.

2. The clown on the red platform has this letter.

3. Look at the ringmaster's hat.

4. This letter is part of the tightrope.

5. This letter is on a juggling pin.

6. A trapeze artist is catching this letter.

7. The poodle has this letter.

8. The clown with the flower has this letter.

9. This letter is on an ice-cream cone.

Which circus performer can see in the dark?

__ __ __ __ __ __ - __ __ __
2   3   4   5   6   7   8   9

Answer on page 31

Groovy Grove

The race moves east, to central Florida. Tripp and Scout hustle straight to an orange grove. Its owner tells them that Florida grows more oranges than anywhere except for Brazil.

"*Orange* you glad to know that," Tripp says to Scout, laughing.

The team's next task is to fill a basket with oranges they pick. "Sweet!" Scout says.

You can help Tripp and Scout! While they pick oranges, use your Florida map to answer the questions. Write each answer in the circle next to the question. When you draw a straight line connecting circles with the same numbers, the line will go through a letter. Read these letters in order from the top left circle to the bottom left circle. They will spell something that Florida produces more of than anywhere else. Find that fact to pick up 20 points on page 29.

What is . . .

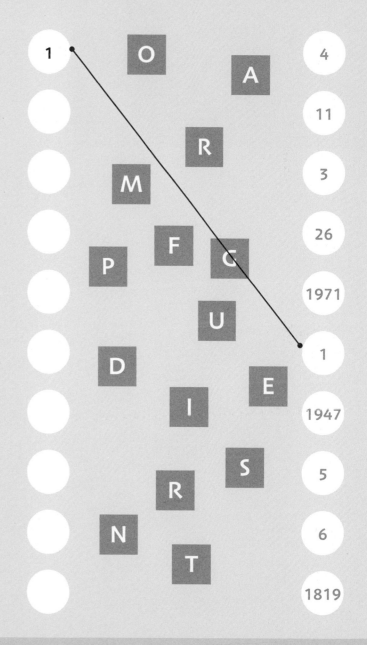

. . . the rank of Jacksonville in population of Florida cities?

. . . the number of words in the name of the state insect?

. . . the interstate highway that goes through Orlando?

. . . the number of feet of rainfall Pensacola gets per year?

. . . the year the Everglades became a national park?

. . . the number of letters in the state bird?

. . . the year the U.S. got Florida from Spain?

. . . the number of states that entered the Union before Florida?

. . . the year that Disney World opened?

. . . the number of times Chris Evert won the U.S. Open?

The Florida item is: G __ __ __ __ __ __ __ __ __ .

Answer on page 31

Space Race

Tripp and Scout speed to their next destination: space camp at the Kennedy Space Center in Cape Canaveral. To train like astronauts, campers put on straps that make them feel weightless. Then they climb up the zero-g wall, like astronauts on a space walk.

Now it's Tripp and Scout's turn to go up the wall. "Houston, we have a problem!" Tripp says. "I'm scared of heights!"

Scout grabs his hand and leads him up, up, and away.

You can help Tripp and Scout! As they climb, solve this out-of-this-world crisscross. Use the number of letters in a word to help figure out where it belongs in the grid. Fill in all 20 words, then look below the grid.

Word List

3 letters
~~SUN~~

4 letters
MARS
MOON
NASA

5 letters
COMET
ORBIT
PLUTO

6 letters
GALAXY
PLANET
ROCKET
SATURN

7 letters
GRAVITY
JUPITER
MERCURY
NEPTUNE

8 letters
ASTEROID

9 letters
ASTRONAUT
BLACK HOLE
SATELLITE
SUPERNOVA

Did you fill in the grid?
Now write the letters from the shaded boxes, in the order they appear in the grid, in the spaces below. They will spell a secret space word—and earn you 10 bonus points on page 29.

__ __ __ __ __ __ __ __ __ __

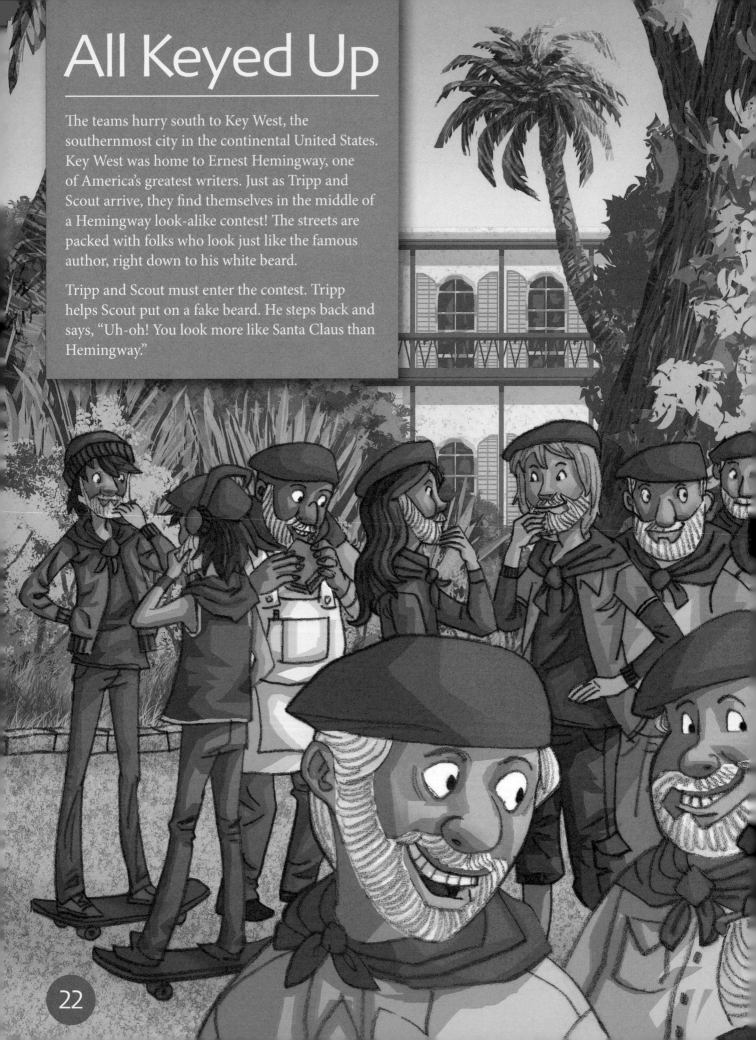

All Keyed Up

The teams hurry south to Key West, the southernmost city in the continental United States. Key West was home to Ernest Hemingway, one of America's greatest writers. Just as Tripp and Scout arrive, they find themselves in the middle of a Hemingway look-alike contest! The streets are packed with folks who look just like the famous author, right down to his white beard.

Tripp and Scout must enter the contest. Tripp helps Scout put on a fake beard. He steps back and says, "Uh-oh! You look more like Santa Claus than Hemingway."

22

You can help Tripp and Scout! While they try to win the contest, use the clues to figure out the words. Each word uses only letters found in ERNEST HEMINGWAY. Figure out all the words to earn 10 points on page 29.

1. Opposite of lose __ __ __

2. *Green Eggs and* _____ __ __ __

3. Oak or maple __ __ __ __

4. The color of snow __ __ __ __ __

5. A horse says this. __ __ __ __ __

6. An angry bee might do this. __ __ __ __ __

7. *Tres* is Spanish for this number. __ __ __ __ __

8. You sip a milkshake through this. __ __ __ __ __ __

9. Valentine shape __ __ __ __ __

10. The coldest season __ __ __ __ __ __

11. A car's motor __ __ __ __ __ __

12. Tie this to a kite. __ __ __ __ __

Answer on page 31

The Glades Maze

The contest heats up as it moves just north to Everglades National Park. This beautiful expanse of wetlands is the only place in the world where crocodiles and alligators exist side by side.

The Which Way crews must race through a maze of waterways. Mel Box and Fred Ex arrive first and take the fastest boat. Tripp and Scout grab a ride on an airboat. "Follow that flamingo!" Scout shouts as they zoom away.

You can help Tripp and Scout! Find the one path from start to finish. Then look at the letters along the correct path. They spell the name of an endangered Everglades animal. The name will earn you 10 points on page 29.

O

R

L

F

H

START

M

A

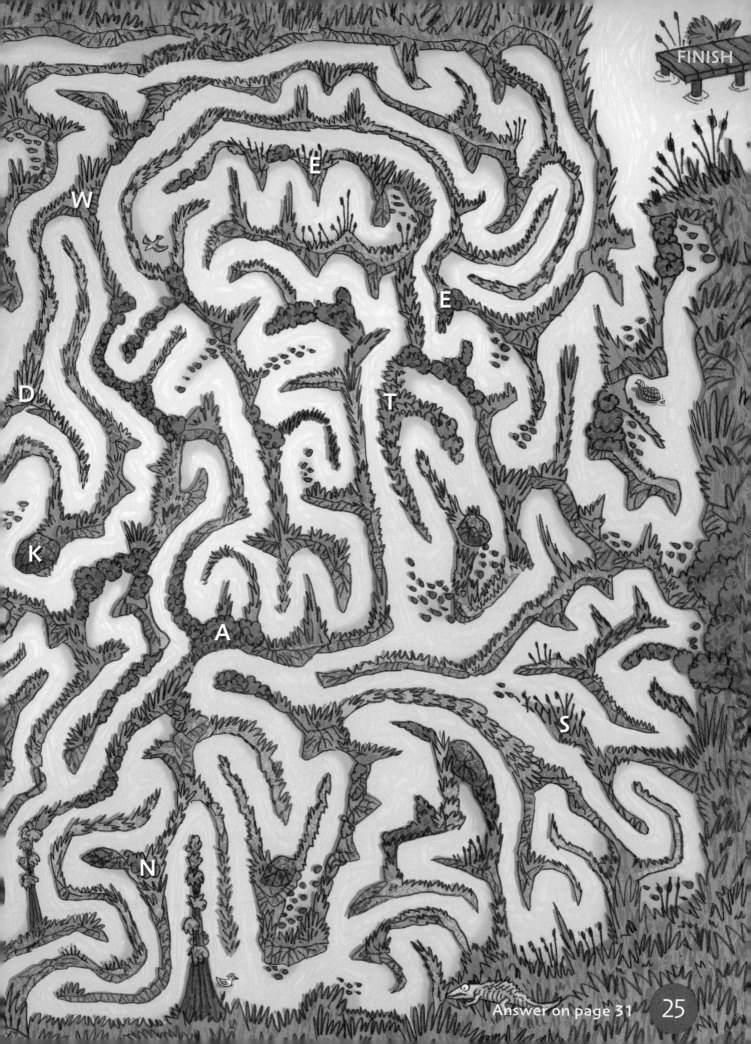

FINISH

Answer on page 31

25

Beach Double

The end of the race is near. Tripp and Scout dash to the next spot, Miami Beach. Florida has more than 800 miles of sandy beaches, and this is the first one the team has hit. But there's no time for a swim. Tripp and Scout must help a professional sand sculptor complete a winning sandcastle. The expert tells the duo to get a shovel and pail—and not to knock anything down!

You can help Tripp and Scout! While they help build the sandcastle, you can dig up the differences in these two pictures. If you spot at least 20, add 10 points on page 29.

Answer on page 31

The Big Finish

Tripp and Scout finish their sandcastle and discover a surprise. The finish line is next to a colorful lifeguard stand right there along the beach! But the good news doesn't last. The Which Way Kids arrive in third place. Mel and Fred were the first to arrive.

"Well, our sandcastle was amazing," Tripp says. "Those last few bonus points will help."

"But will they be enough to win?" Scout asks.

You Helped Tripp and Scout!

Keep track of the bonus points you have earned. Check each puzzle you finish. When you complete the Florida race, add up the bonus points next to the boxes you checked.

Page 4	And They're Off!	I finished the maze.	10	☐
Page 6	Fowl Play	I answered the riddle.	10	☐
Page 8	Spring Fever	I answered all the questions.	20	☐
Page 10	Spitting Images	I matched 10 slices.	10	☐
Page 12	Hide and Seek	I found the hidden objects.	10	☐
Page 14	Screwball Baseball	I circled 20 silly things.	10	☐
Page 16	Clowning Around	I answered the riddle.	10	☐
Page 18	Groovy Grove	I figured out the fun fact.	20	☐
Page 20	Space Race	I found the space word.	10	☐
Page 22	All Keyed Up	I wrote 12 words.	10	☐
Page 24	The Glades Maze	I found the animal's name.	10	☐
Page 26	Beach Double	I circled 20 differences.	10	☐

My total bonus points to add to Tripp and Scout's score: ☐

Did you earn enough bonus points to help Tripp and Scout win the race? Turn to page 32 and find out!

Answers

4 And They're Off!

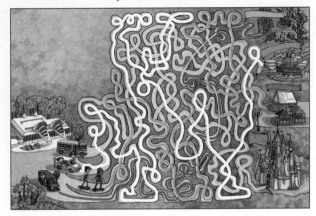

6 Fowl Play

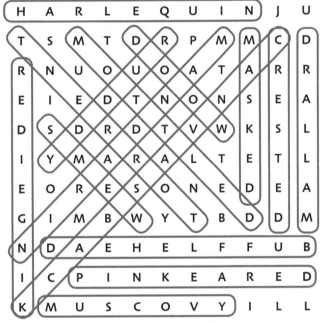

JUST PUT IT ON MY BILL.

8 Spring Fever

1. b	6. c
2. b	7. c
3. a	8. b
4. c	9. a
5. b	10. b

10 Spitting Images

12 Hide and Seek

14 Screwball Baseball

16 Clowning Around

AN ACRO-BAT

18 Groovy Grove

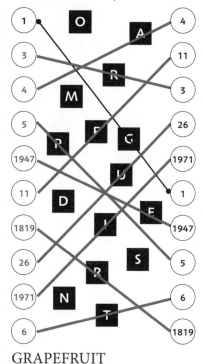

GRAPEFRUIT

20 Space Race

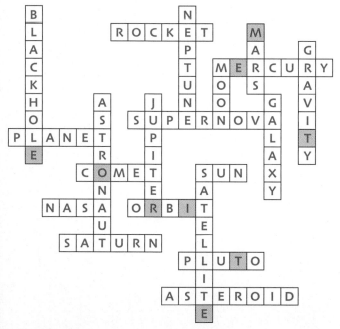

METEORITE

22 All Keyed Up

1. WIN
2. HAM
3. TREE
4. WHITE
5. NEIGH
6. STING
7. THREE
8. STRAW
9. HEART
10. WINTER
11. ENGINE
12. STRING

24 The Glades Maze

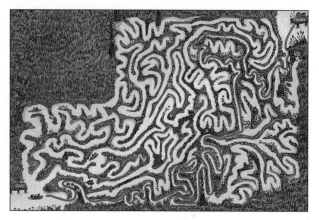

MANATEE

26 Beach Double

And the Winner Is . . .

Tripp and Scout earned 150 points for finishing third. Write your bonus points in the box and add that to their total. Did they win the race?

Scout, want to see the photos I took in the Everglades?

Later, gator!

Don't forget to write the final results on the Florida page of your game guide.

OFFICIAL GAME GUIDE

Highlights

WHICH WAY USA

Rules of the Road • Player Profiles • State-by-State Tracker

FINISHERS	Mel Box and Fred Ex	Zig and Zag	Tripp and Scout	Kareem Cheese and Shelly
SCORE	200	175	150	125
BONUS POINTS	20	60		130
FINAL TOTAL	*220*	*235*		*255*